CONTENTS

PIGEONS

and other City Poems

Compiled and illustrated by

ANNIE OWEN

M
MACMILLAN CHILDREN'S BOOKS

FOR ALEX AND LEONIE

Illustrations © Annie Owen 1992

First published 1992 by
PAN MACMILLAN CHILDREN'S BOOKS
A division of Pan Macmillan Limited
Cavaye Place London SW10 9PG
Associated companies throughout the world

ISBN 0-333-56361-1

A CIP catalogue record for this book
is available from the British Library

Photoset by Rowland Phototypesetting Limited,
Bury St Edmunds, Suffolk
Printed in Hong Kong

VICTORIA STATION 6.58 P.M.

Mervyn Peake

Sudden, beneath the pendant clock arose
Out of the drab and artificial ground
A horse with wings of scarlet, and pale flowers
Glimmered upon his forehead, while around

His neck and mane like wreaths of incense streamed
Young hosts of stars, and as his eyes burned proud,
The men with black umbrellas stood and stared
And nudged each other and then laughed aloud.

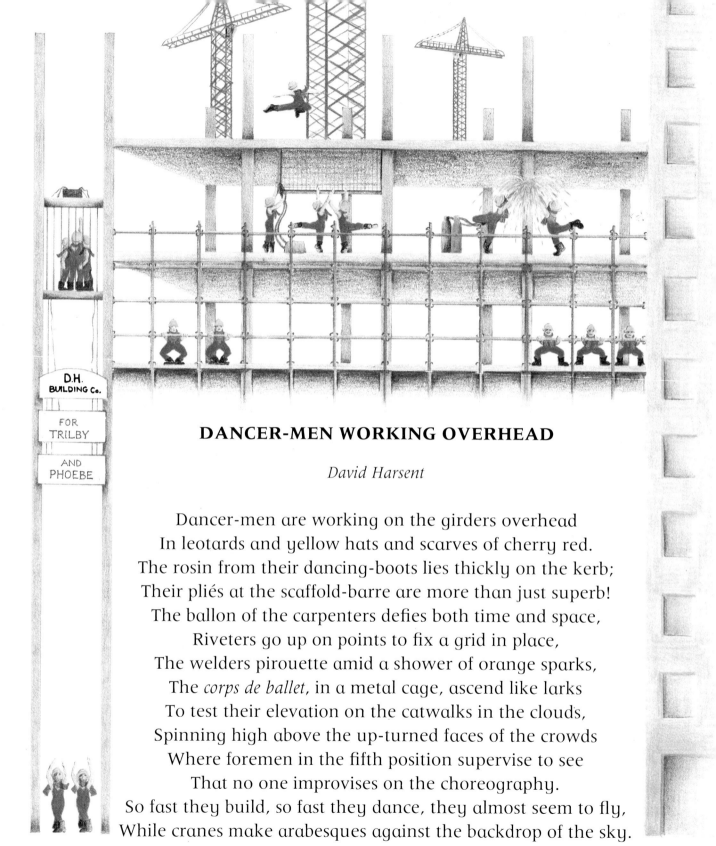

DANCER-MEN WORKING OVERHEAD

David Harsent

Dancer-men are working on the girders overhead
In leotards and yellow hats and scarves of cherry red.
The rosin from their dancing-boots lies thickly on the kerb;
Their pliés at the scaffold-barre are more than just superb!
The ballon of the carpenters defies both time and space,
Riveters go up on points to fix a grid in place,
The welders pirouette amid a shower of orange sparks,
The *corps de ballet*, in a metal cage, ascend like larks
To test their elevation on the catwalks in the clouds,
Spinning high above the up-turned faces of the crowds
Where foremen in the fifth position supervise to see
That no one improvises on the choreography.
So fast they build, so fast they dance, they almost seem to fly,
While cranes make arabesques against the backdrop of the sky.

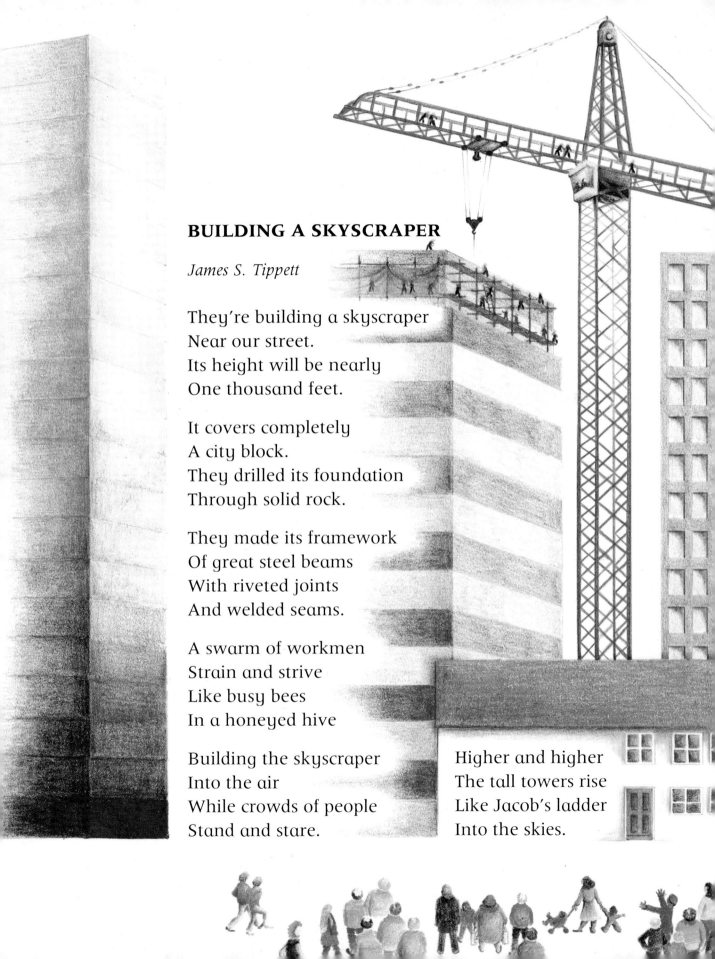

BUILDING A SKYSCRAPER

James S. Tippett

They're building a skyscraper
Near our street.
Its height will be nearly
One thousand feet.

It covers completely
A city block.
They drilled its foundation
Through solid rock.

They made its framework
Of great steel beams
With riveted joints
And welded seams.

A swarm of workmen
Strain and strive
Like busy bees
In a honeyed hive

Building the skyscraper
Into the air
While crowds of people
Stand and stare.

Higher and higher
The tall towers rise
Like Jacob's ladder
Into the skies.

SOME RESIDENTS OF RHUBARB STREET

Richard Edwards

Michelle, who lives at number 4,
Looked out one Christmas Eve and saw
A carol-singing dinosaur.
It's true, I know,
She told me so.

And Marge, who lives at number 10,
Each midnight turns into a hen,
Clucks twice and then turns back again.
It's true, I know,
She told me so.

And Fran, who lives at number 2,
Walked into church and found her pew
Swarming with sea-lions from the zoo.
It's true, I know,
She told me so.

And Luke, who lives at number 3,
Was once imprisoned in a tree
Till six woodpeckers pecked him free.
It's true, I know,
He told me so.

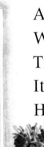

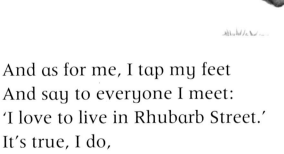

And as for me, I tap my feet
And say to everyone I meet:
'I love to live in Rhubarb Street.'
It's true, I do,
Well, wouldn't you?

PIGEONS

Richard Kell

They paddle with staccato feet
In powder-pools of sunlight,
Small blue busybodies
Strutting like fat gentlemen
With hands clasped
Under their swallowtail coats;
And, as they stump about,
Their heads like tiny hammers
Tap at imaginary nails
In non-existent walls.
Elusive ghosts of sunshine
Slither down the green gloss
Of their necks an instant, and are gone.

Summer hangs drugged from sky to earth
In limpid fathoms of silence:
Only warm dark dimples of sound
Slide like slow bubbles
From the contented throats.

Raise a casual hand –
With one quick gust
They fountain into air.

THE PEOPLE UPSTAIRS

Ogden Nash

The people upstairs all practice ballet.

Their living room is a bowling alley.

Their bedroom is full of conducted tours.

Their radio is louder than yours.

They celebrate weekends all the week.

When they take a shower your ceilings leak.

They try to get their parties to mix
By supplying their guests with pogo sticks.

And when their orgy at last abates
They go to the bathroom on roller skates.

I might love the people upstairs wondrous
If instead of above us, they just lived under us.

14

MOTOR CARS

Rowena Bastin Bennett

From city window, way up high,
I like to watch the cars go by.
They look like burnished beetles, black,
That leave a little muddy track
Behind them as they slowly crawl.
Sometimes they do not move at all
But huddle close with hum and drone
As though they feared to be alone.
They grope their way through fog and night
With the golden feelers of their light.

LOLLIPOP LADY

John Agard

Lollipop lady,
lollipop lady,
wave your magic stick
and make the traffic
stop a while
so we can cross the street.

Trucks and cars
rushing past
have no time for little feet.
They hate to wait
especially when late
but we'll be late too
except for you.

So lollipop lady, lollipop lady
in the middle of the street
wave your magic stick
and make the traffic
give way to little feet.

THE REVOLT OF THE LAMP POSTS

Mike Harding

Last night I saw the lamp posts
That light up our back street
Wiggle, and then wriggle
And then, suddenly, they'd feet.

Then they all cleared off and left us,
The whole street in the dark,
So I left the house and followed,
There were millions in the park.

All the lamps from miles around
Had run away tonight,
They were dancing, they were singing,
And they held each other tight.

The king, a big green lamp post
Said 'No more workin' brothers!
We'll leave them humings in the dark
And they'll bump into each other.

Just think about them walkin' round
With black eyes and broke noses
No more dogs to wet your feet
No more rusty toeses!

See, I've been a lamp post all me life, but
Now me mantle's growin' dim,
They'll chuck me on the scrap heap
It's a shame! a crime! a sin!'

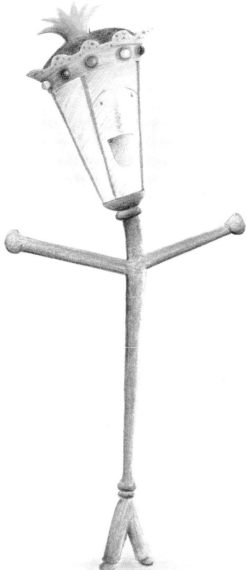

The other lamp posts muttered
And began to hiss and boo,
'Let's march upon the Town Hall
That's what we ought to do!'

The Lord Mayor he was woken
By a terribobble sight,
When he opened up his window,
Didn't he get a fright!

There were twenty million lamp posts
And the light as bright as day
And the young lamp posts were shoutin' out
'Free Speech and Equal Pay! –

New Mantles Every Quarter!'
'I agree,' the Lord Mayor cried
'To everything you ask for!'
Then he quickly ran inside.

So I watched the lamp posts go back home,
As quickly as they came
And with the first light of the day,
They were in their holes again.

Now there's an old age home for lamp posts
And an old age pension scheme
And every month they're painted
With a coat of glossy green,

New mantles every couple of months,
And they stand up straighter too,
And only the Lord Mayor knows why,
Him, and me, and twenty million lamp posts,

And a couple of hundred dogs, and you!

STREET CRICKET

Gareth Owen

On August evenings by the lamp post
When the days are long and light
The lads come out for cricket
And play until it's night.
They bat and bowl and field and shout
And someone shouts 'HOWZAT!'
But you can't give Peter Batty out
Or he'll take away his bat.

The dogs in the Close all love to field
And chase about the street.
The stumper wears his mother's gloves
And stops the ball with his feet.
Everyone should have a bowl
That's the proper way to play
But Batty has to bowl all night
Or he takes his ball away.

When lamps and rooms turn on their lights
And you can hardly see the ball
The lads begin to drift off home
You can hear the goodbyes they call.
But Peter Batty's two hundred not out
And he shouts as he walks away,
'Remember I'm batting tomorrow night
Or I won't let anyone play.'

MY FATHER OWNS THE BUTCHER SHOP

Anon

My father owns the butcher shop,
My mother cuts the meat,
And I'm the little hot dog
That runs around the street.

ALLEY CAT

Anon

A bit of jungle in the street.
He goes on velvet toes
And, slinking through the shadows, stalks
Imaginary foes.

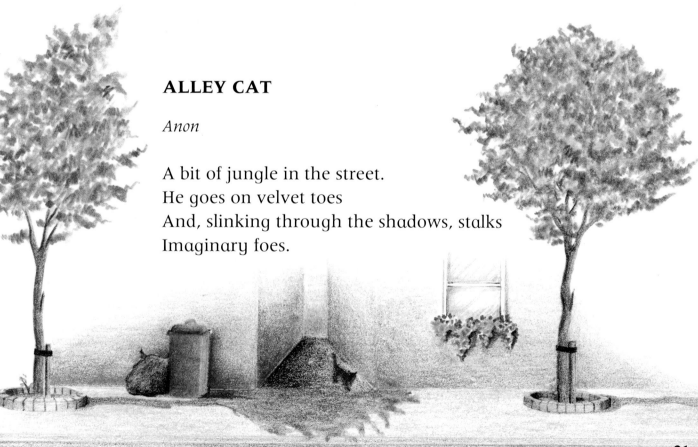

MRS BUTTON

James Reeves

When Mrs Button, of a morning,
Comes creaking down the street,
You hear her old two black boots whisper
'Poor feet – poor feet – poor feet!'

When Mrs Button, every Monday,
Sweeps the chapel neat,
All down the long, hushed aisles they whisper
'Poor feet – poor feet – poor feet!'

Mrs Button after dinner
(It is her Sunday treat)
Sits down and takes her two black boots off
And rests her two poor feet.

SUNKEN EVENING

Laurie Lee

The green light floods the city square –
   A sea of fowl and feathered fish,
   Where squalls of rainbirds dive and splash
And gusty sparrows chop the air.

Submerged, the prawn-blue pigeons feed
   In sandy grottoes round the Mall,
   And crusted lobster-buses crawl
Among the fountains' silver weed.

There, like a wreck, with mast and bell,
   The torn church settles by the bow,
   While phosphorescent starlings stow
Their mussel shells along the hull.

The oyster-poet, drowned but dry,
   Rolls a black pearl between his bones;
   The typist, trapped by telephones,
Gazes in bubbles at the sky.

Till, with the dark, the shallows run,
   And homeward surges tide and fret –
   The slow night trawls its heavy net
And hauls the clerk to Surbiton.

e. e. cummings

who knows if the moon's
a balloon, coming out of a keen city
in the sky – filled with pretty people?
(and if you and i should

get into it, if they
should take me and take you into their balloon,
why then
we'd go up higher with all the pretty people

than houses and steeples and clouds:
go sailing
away and away sailing into a keen
city which nobody's ever visited, where

always
          it's
                Spring) and everyone's
in love and flowers pick themselves

SNOW IN THE SUBURBS

Thomas Hardy

Every branch big with it,
Bent every twig with it;
Every fork like a white web-foot;
Every street and pavement mute:
Some flakes have lost their way, and grope back upward, when
Meeting those meandering down they turn and descend again.
The palings are glued together like a wall,
And there is no waft of wind with the fleecy fall.

A sparrow enters the tree,
Whereon immediately
A snow lump thrice his size
Descends on him and showers his head and eyes,
And overturns him,
And near inurns him,
And lights on a nether twig, when its brush
Starts off a volley and other lodging lumps with a rush.

The steps are a blanched slope,
Up which, with feeble hope,
A black cat comes, wide-eyed and thin;
And we take him in.

JUST BEFORE CHRISTMAS

Kit Wright

Down the Holloway Road on the top of the bus
On the just-before-Christmas nights we go,
Allie and me and all of us,
And we look at the lit-up shops below.
Orange and yellow the fruit stalls glow,
Store windows are sploshed with sort-of snow,
And Santa's a poor old so-and-so,
With his sweating gear and his sack in tow,
And Christ . . . mas is coming!

At the front of the top of the lit-up bus
Way down the Holloway Road we ride,
Allie and me and all of us,
And the butchers chop and lop with pride,
And the turkeys squat with their stuffing inside
By ropes of sausages soon to be fried,
And every door is open wide
As down the road we growl or glide
And Christ . . . mas is coming!

All at the front of the top of the bus,
Far down the Holloway Road we roar,
Allie and me and all of us,
And tellies are tinselled in every store,
With fairy lights over every door,
With glitter and crêpe inside, what's more,
And everyone seeming to say, 'For sure,
Christmas is coming like never before.'
Yes, Christ . . . mas is coming!

SIDEWALK PACERS

Lillian Morrison

Hey, sidewalk pacers,
bumper riders
long-legged gliders,
stalkers, ledge walkers
roof straddlers
fence jumpers
stompers, trouncers,
muggers, sluggers,
big burly bouncers,
alley runners,
stabbers, purse grabbers,
hurriers, harriers,
scared scurriers,
all chased and chasers
please cease for a moment.
Oh please,
lie down in a heap
and sleep.

COPYRIGHT ACKNOWLEDGEMENTS

The compiler and publishers would like to thank the following for permission to reprint the selections in this book. All possible care has been taken to trace the ownership of every selection included and to make full acknowledgement for its use. If any errors have accidentally occurred, they will be corrected in subsequent editions, provided notification is sent to the publishers.

The Bodley Head Ltd for 'Lollipop Lady' by John Agard from *I Din Do Nuttin*. Reprinted by permission of The Bodley Head Ltd.

Modern Curriculum Press, Inc., for 'Motor Cars' by Rowena Bastin Bennett from *Songs Around a Toadstool Table* © Rowena Bastin Bennett 1967. Reprinted by permission of Modern Curriculum Press, Inc.

Grafton Books, part of HarperCollins Publishers, for 'who knows if the moon's' by e. e. cummings from *Complete Poems 1910–1962*. Reprinted by permission of HarperCollins Publishers.

'who knows if the moon's' is reprinted from *Tulips & Chimneys* by e. e. cummings, edited by George James Firmage, by permission of Liveright Publishing Corporation. Copyright 1923, 1925 and renewed 1951, 1953 by e. e. cummings. Copyright © 1973, 1976 by the Trustees for the e. e. cummings Trust. Copyright © 1973, 1976 by George James Firmage.

Orchard Books for 'Some Residents of Rhubarb Street' by Richard Edwards from *A Mouse in My Roof*. Reprinted by permission of Orchard Books, 96 Leonard Street, London EC2A 4RH.

Moonraker Productions Ltd for 'The Revolt of the Lamp Posts' by Mike Harding from *Up the Boo Aye, Shooting Pookakies*. Reprinted by permission of Moonraker Productions Ltd.

David Harsent for 'Dancer-Men Working Overhead' by David Harsent. Reprinted by permission of David Harsent.

The Bodley Head Ltd for 'Pigeons' by Richard Kell from *Differences* by Richard Kell. Reprinted by permission of The Bodley Head Ltd.

Andre Deutsch Ltd for 'Sunken Evening' by Laurie Lee from *My Many-Coated Man* © Laurie Lee 1955, Andre Deutsch Ltd, and *Selected Poems* © Laurie Lee 1983, Andre Deutsch Ltd. Reprinted by permission.

Curtis Brown Ltd for 'The People Upstairs' by Ogden Nash from *Versus* © 1949 by Ogden Nash. Reprinted by permission of Curtis Brown Ltd.

HarperCollins Publishers for 'Street Cricket' by Gareth Owen from *Song of the City*. Reprinted by permission of HarperCollins Publishers.

David Higham Associates for 'Victoria Station 6.58 p.m.' from *Selected Poems*, published by Faber & Faber Ltd. Reprinted by permission of David Higham Associates.

The James Reeves Estate for 'Mrs Button' from *The Wandering Moon and Other Poems*, published by Puffin Books. © James Reeves. Reprinted by permission of The James Reeves Estate.

Penguin Books Ltd for 'Just Before Christmas' by Kit Wright from *Cat Among the Pigeons*, published by Viking Kestrel. © Kit Wright 1987. Reprinted by permission of Penguin Books Ltd.